Play Easy Recorder

Published by:
Chester Music Limited
8/9 Frith Street, London W1D 3JB, England.

Exclusive distributors:
Music Sales Limited
Distribution Centre, Newmarket Road,
Bury St Edmunds, Suffolk IP33 3YB.

Music Sales Pty Limited
120 Rothschild Avenue, Rosebery,
NSW 2018, Australia.

Order No. CH67595
ISBN 1-84449-297-4
This book © Copyright 2003 by Chester Music.

All arrangements by Jerry Lanning.
Music engraved by Jerry Lanning.

www.musicsales.com

Chester Music Limited
London / New York / Paris / Sydney /
Copenhagen / Berlin / Madrid / Tokyo

Volume 3

Oh Mary, Don't You Weep

American Gospel Song

Quite brightly ♩ = 120

Oh Mar - y, don't you weep, don't you mourn. Oh Mar - y, don't you
weep, don't you mourn. Phar - aoh's ar - my got drown - ded; Oh Mar - y, don't you
weep. If I could I sure - ly would_ stand on the rock where Mo - ses stood._
Phar - aoh's ar - my got drown - ded; Oh Mar - y, don't you weep.

Banks Of The Ohio

American Traditional

Moderately ♩ = 120

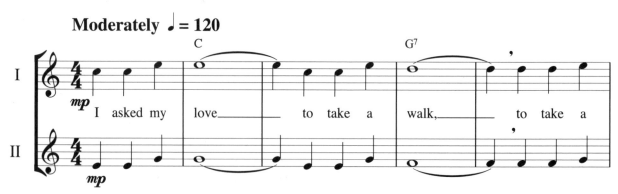

I asked my love____ to take a walk,____ to take a

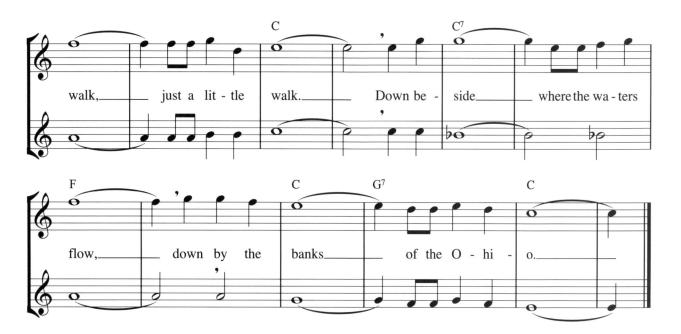

walk, just a lit-tle walk. Down be-side where the wa-ters flow, down by the banks of the O-hi-o.

Over The Waves (Sobre Los Olas)

By Juventino Rosas

Brightly ♩. = 60

The Bare Necessities

(from "The Jungle Book")
Words & Music by Terry Gilkyson

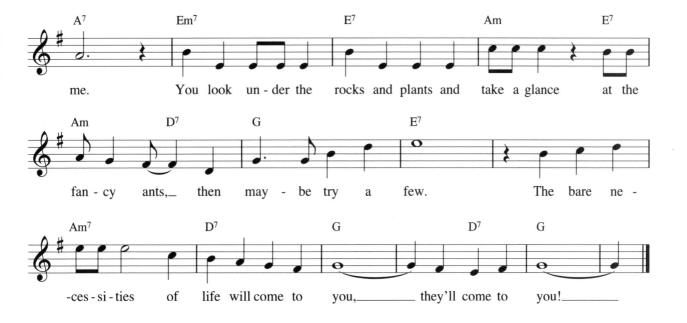

me. You look un-der the rocks and plants and take a glance at the

fan-cy ants,_ then may-be try a few. The bare ne-

-ces-si-ties of life will come to you,_____ they'll come to you!_____

Here Comes The Bride

(Bridal Chorus from "Lohengrin")
By Richard Wagner

Bring Me Sunshine

Words by Sylvia Dee
Music by Arthur Kent

Guantanamera

Words adapted by Julian Orbon from a poem by José Marti
Music adaptation by Pete Seeger & Julian Orbon

Fernando

Words & Music by Benny Andersson, Björn Ulvaeus & Stig Anderson

I Came, I Saw, I Conga'd

Words & Music by James Cavanaugh, John Redmond & Frank Weldon

10

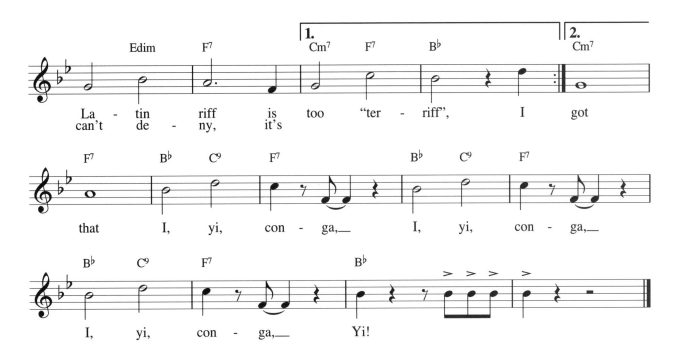

La - tin riff is too "ter - riff", I got
can't de - ny, it's

that I, yi, con - ga,___ I, yi, con - ga,___

I, yi, con - ga,___ Yi!

The Skater's Waltz

By Emil Waldteufel

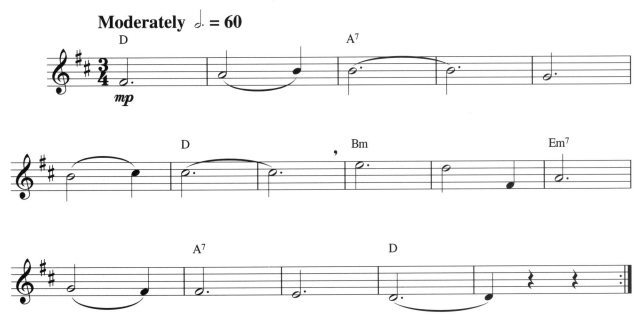

It's Now Or Never

Music by Eduardo di Capua
Words by Aaron Schroeder & Wally Gold

When I first saw you,___ with your smile so ten - der,

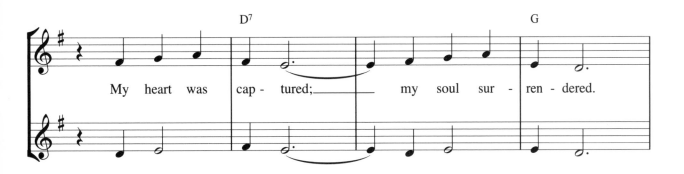

My heart was cap - tured;___ my soul sur - ren - dered.

I've spent a life - time___ wait - ing for the right time.

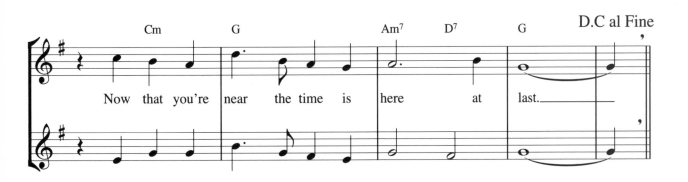

Now that you're near the time is here at last.___

Light My Fire

Words & Music by Jim Morrison, Robbie Krieger, Ray Manzarek & John Densmore

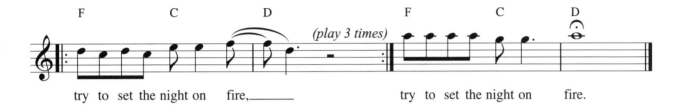

try to set the night on fire,_____ try to set the night on fire.

Allelujah

(from "Exsultate Jubilate")
By W. A. Mozart

Quite brightly ♩ = 108

Love Theme From "The Godfather"

By Nino Rota

My Favourite Things

(from "The Sound Of Music")
Words by Oscar Hammerstein II
Music by Richard Rodgers

Memory

(from "Cats")
Music by Andrew Lloyd Webber
Lyrics by Trevor Nunn after T.S. Eliot

new life___ and I must-n't give in.___ When the dawn comes to-night will be a

me - mo - ry too___ and a new day will be - gin.

Theme From "E.T. (The Extra-Terrestrial)"

By John Williams

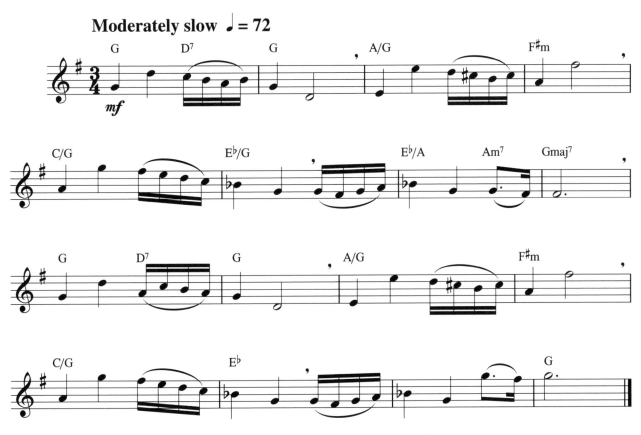

Mull Of Kintyre

Words & Music by Paul McCartney & Denny Laine

Mull of Kintyre,
Oh mist rolling in from the sea,
My desire is always to be here,
Oh Mull of Kintyre.

Far have I travelled and much have I seen,
Dark distant mountains with valleys of green.
Past painted deserts, the sunset's on fire
As he carries me home to the Mull of Kintyre.

My Heart Will Go On

(from "Titanic")
Words by Will Jennings
Music by James Horner

22

Old Folks At Home

Words & Music by Stephen Foster

Moderately slow ♩ = 80

Way down up-on the Swan-ee riv-er, far, far a-way,

there's where my heart is turn-ing ev-er, there's where the old folks stay.

All up and down the whole cre-a-tion, sad-ly I roam,

still long-ing for the old plan-ta-tion, and for the old folks at home.

All the world is sad and drear-y Ev-'ry-where I roam.

Oh, how my heart is grow-ing wear-y, far from the old folks at home.

Skip To My Lou

American Traditional

Brightly ♩ = 108

Skip, skip, skip to my Lou. Skip, skip,

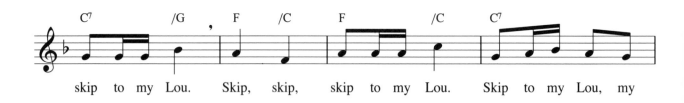

skip to my Lou. Skip, skip, skip to my Lou. Skip to my Lou, my

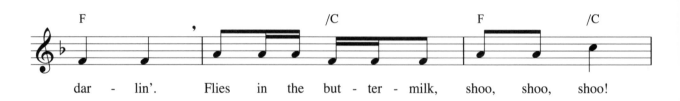

dar - lin'. Flies in the but - ter - milk, shoo, shoo, shoo!

Flies in the but - ter - milk, shoo, shoo, shoo! Flies in the but - ter - milk,

shoo, shoo shoo! Skip to my Lou, my dar - lin'.

The Sleeping Beauty Waltz

By Pyotr Ilyich Tchaikovsky

She'll Be Comin' 'Round The Mountain

American Traditional

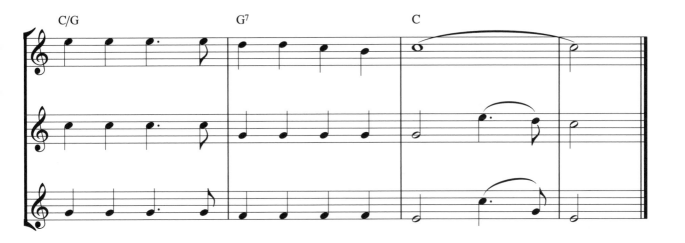

She'll be comin' 'round the mountain when she comes,
She'll be comin' 'round the mountain when she comes,
She'll be comin' 'round the mountain, she'll be comin' 'round the mountain,
She'll be comin' 'round the mountain when she comes.

Shenandoah

American Traditional

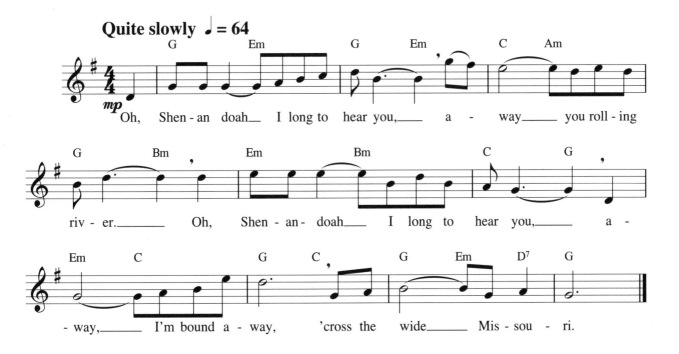

Quite slowly ♩ = 64

Oh, Shen-an doah__ I long to hear you,__ a - way__ you roll-ing riv - er.__ Oh, Shen-an-doah__ I long to hear you,__ a - way,__ I'm bound a - way, 'cross the wide__ Mis - sou - ri.

Spring

(from "The Four Seasons")
By Antonio Vivaldi

Hush Little Baby

American Traditional

Moderately ♩ = 60

Hush, lit - tle ba - by, don't say a word, Pop - pa's gon - na buy you a mock - ing bird.

If that mock - ing bird don't sing, Pop - pa's gon - na buy you a dia - mond ring.

Two Little Boys

Words by Edward Madden
Music by Theodore Morse

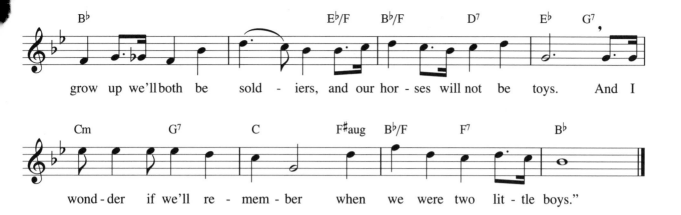

grow up we'll both be sold - iers, and our hor - ses will not be toys. And I

wond - der if we'll re - mem - ber when we were two lit - tle boys."

Worried Man Blues

American Traditional

Steady ♩ = 132

It takes a wor - ried man to sing a wor - ried song, It

takes a wor - ried man to sing a wor - ried song, It

takes a wor - ried man to sing a wor - ried song, I'm wor - ried

now, but I won't be wor - ried long.

Trumpet Voluntary

By Jeremiah Clarke